PUMPKIN GRUMPKIN

To the memory of Sukumar Ray who embraced
Nonsense with Bengali arms

First published 2011 by Walker Books Ltd
87 Vauxhall Walk, London SE11 5HJ

2 4 6 8 10 9 7 5 3 1

Introduction and anthology © 2011 John Agard and Grace Nichols
Poems © individual poet
Illustrations © 2011 Satoshi Kitamura

This book has been typeset in Triplex and Interlude

Printed and bound in Great Britain by Clays Ltd, St Ives plc

British Library Cataloguing in Publication Data:
a catalogue record for this book is available from the British Library

ISBN 978-1-4063-0888-4

www.walker.co.uk

PUMPKIN GRUMPKIN
Nonsense Poems from Around the World

collected by
John Agard & Grace Nichols

illustrated by
Satoshi Kitamura

WALKER
BOOKS

Contents

INTRODUCTION

It was while in India that we came across **Abol Tabol**, a book of nonsense poems by Sukumar Ray (translated by Sampurna Chattarji). Born in Bengal in 1923, Sukumar Ray wrote and illustrated a number of books for children. He even founded a Nonsense Club.

To come across nonsense poems in India took us by surprise and we were excited to read that Edward Lear, famous for one of the greatest nonsense poems of all, "The Owl And The Pussycat," had lived in India and drawn inspiration for nonsense poems from Hindi words. And soon we were hooked on the idea of putting together an anthology of nonsense poems from various cultures.

Having grown up in Guyana (then British Guiana) in the Caribbean, we had got a taste for nonsense through English poetry and nursery rhymes as well as from funny calypso songs, which often had bits of nonsense influence – like the one about the policeman who arrested himself for breaking the law and, being a magistrate also, put himself on trial and sentenced himself. It was a case of himself arresting himself and sentencing himself.

But there's more to nonsense than meets the ear.

In Russia, the poet Daniil Kharms was arrested in 1931 and then imprisoned because the authorities were suspicious of his writing and saw his nonsense as disguised criticism. And not only can nonsense be seen as politically threatening, but it can also serve as a tool of wisdom, the way nonsense riddles (koans) are used by Japanese Zen masters to test young monks: "What is the sound of one hand clapping?" It boggles the mind and that's exactly what it's meant to do.

A bit of mind boggling brings you to the enlightened realization that not everything in life can be solved by the two-plus-two-equals-four mind.

For lovers of language, nonsense poems can do strange and Jabberwocky things with words, often producing new ones, as Lewis Carroll famously did.

Some modern poets such as Colin West are driven by the Muse of Nonsense, but even those who don't specialize in it find a dose of it can be healthy. T. S. Eliot, for instance, wrote about grim post-war Britain, yet he also drew inspiration from a bunch of cats up to nonsensical shenanigans.

So welcome to the world of **Pumpkin Grumpkin**, where topsy-turvy lives in harmony with upside down!

John Agard and Grace Nichols

Sounds of Asia

In Japan dogs go "wan-wan".

Chinese dogs go "wan-wan".

Dogs of Vietnam go "gaw-gaw".

In the Philippines dogs go "baw-waw".

Indonesian dogs go "gug-gug".

Dogs of Mongolia go "hofu-hofu".

And Thai dogs go "hon-hon".

Please let me know how dogs go in your country.

Please let me feel the sounds of Asia all over Asia.

In Japan cats go "nyao".

Chinese cats go "miyao".

Cats of Vietnam go "mew-mew".

In the Philippines cats go "ngiaw".

Indonesian cats go "meiohg".

Cats of Mongolia go "myau".

And Thai cats go "meo-meo".

Please let me know how cats go in your country.

Please let me feel the sounds of Asia all over Asia.

In Japan cows go "mo".

Chinese cows go "ma".

Cows of Vietnam go "o-o".

In the Philippines cows go "ngna-ngna".

Indonesian cows go "em-em".

Cows of Mongolia go "umu-umu".

And Thai cows go "woa-woa".

Please let me know how cows go in your country.

Please let me feel the sounds of Asia all over Asia.

Takashi Arima (Japan)

Er....

Hindi Class

The creatures learning Hindi
Kicked up quite a shindy.
From amidst all the brouhaha
The jackal asked, "Kya hua?"
Joining the abysmal howl
"Han han hoon," said the owl.
Not to be left out at that
"Main aoon?" asked the cat.

J.P. Das (India)

Coati-Mundi

As I went walking one fine Sunday,
I happened to meet a Coati-Mundi.
   "Coati-Mundi," I said,
   "It's a lovely Sunday
As sure as you're a Coati-Mundi,
A handsome, long-tailed Coati-Mundi
   With eyes peering out,
   A flexible snout,
And a raccoon coat all furry and bundly!"

"I quite agree," said the Coati-Mundi,
"It is indeed a most beautiful Sunday.
   What joy for the eye!
   What clouds! What sky!
   What fields of rye!
   Oh, never have I
In all my life seen such a Sunday!"

So he took my hand, and we walked together,
I and my friend, the Coati-Mundi,
Enjoying that most unusual weather,
Enjoying that most delightful Sunday.

William Jay Smith (USA)

Up from Down Under

The boomerang and kangaroo
comprise a very pleasant two;
the coolibah and billabong
together make a sort of song.
But tasty as a fresh meringue
is billabong with boomerang;
and better than hooray-hoorah
is kangaroo with coolibah.

David McCord (USA)

Too Many Daves

Did I ever tell you that Mrs McCave

Had twenty-three sons and she named them all Dave?

Well, she did. And that wasn't a smart thing to do.

You see, when she wants one and calls out, "Yoo-Hoo!

Come into the house, Dave!" she doesn't get one.

All twenty-three Daves of hers come on the run!

This makes things quite difficult at the McCaves'

As you can imagine, with so many Daves.

And often she wishes that when they were born,

She had named one of them Bodkin Van Horn.

And one of them Hoo-Foos. And one of them Snimm.

And one of them Hot-Shot. And one Sunny Jim.

And one of them Shadrack. And one of them Blinkey.

And one of them Stuffy. And one of them Stinkey.

Another one Putt-Putt. Another one Moon-Face.

Another one Marvin O'Gravel Balloon Face.

And one of them Ziggy. And one Soggy Muff.

One Buffalo Bill. And one Biffalo Buff.

And one of them Sneepy. And one Weepy Weed.

And one Paris Garters. And one Harris Tweed.

And one of them Sir Michael Carmichael Zutt.

And one of them Oliver Boliver Butt.

And one of them Zanzibar Buck-Buck McFate…

But she didn't do it. And now it's too late.

Dr Seuss (USA)

"I LIKE NONSENSE. IT WAKES UP THE BRAIN CELLS."
Dr Seuss

I Shall Tell A Silly Tale

I shall tell a silly tale:

The dog jumped over the milking pail.

A second tale I shall tell:

The water poured from the weeping well.

The third that I shall tell to you:

The children slept in the chimney flue.

And when they had slept a long, long time

They were fed with bread and told this rhyme!

(Traditional, Czech Republic)
Translated by **Andrew Fusek Peters**

The Carcajou and the Kincajou

They tell me of a distant zoo

Where a carcajou met a kincajou.

Full soon to savage blows they came

From laughing at each other's name.

The agile ajous fought till dark

And carc slew kinc and kinc slew carc,

And beside the conquered kincajou

Lay the carcass of the carcajou.

Ogden Nash (USA)

The Puffin Who Lived In A Muffin

There once was a black and white puffin

Who lived in a blueberry muffin.

Blueberries were the halls

and all of the walls.

Believe you me, I am not bluffin'.

Puffin came home real late

And he ate and he ate and he ate

One blueberry, two blueberry and more.

He ate up the walls and all of the halls

till his house was nuffin but floor.

The little black and white puffin

He so loved the taste of blueberry muffins

that his house became nuffin but nuffin.

Yansan Agard (Guyana/USA)

One Fine October Morning

One fine October morning
In September, last July,
The moon lay thick upon the ground,
The snow shone in the sky.
The flowers were singing gaily
And the birds were in full bloom.
I went down to the cellar
To sweep the upstairs room.

(Traditional, England)

One Fine Day
In The Middle Of The Night

One fine day in the middle of the night

Two dead men began to fight.

Two blind men to see fair play,

One dumb man to shout hooray.

A lame-foot donkey passing by

Kicked the man in he left right eye.

(Traditional, Guyana)

On the Ning Nang Nong

On the Ning Nang Nong

Where the Cows go Bong!

And the Monkeys all say Boo!

There's a Nong Nang Ning

Where the trees go Ping!

And the tea pots Jibber Jabber Joo.

On the Nong Ning Nang

All the mice go Clang!

And you just can't catch 'em when they do!

So it's Ning Nang Nong!

Cows go Bong!

Nong Nang Ning!

Trees go Ping!

Nong Ning Nang!

The mice go Clang!

What a noisy place to belong

Is the Ning Nang Ning Nang Nong!!

Spike Milligan (England)

"I notice that nonsense is always acceptable to the young - clowning is part of nonsense."

SPIKE MILLIGAN

Anna Elise

Anna Elise,

she jumped with surprise;

The surprise was so quick,

it played her a trick;

The trick was so rare,

she jumped on a chair;

The chair was so frail,

she jumped in a pail;

The pail was so wet,

she jumped in a net;

The net was so small,

she jumped on a ball;

The ball was so round,

she jumped on the ground;

And ever since then

she's been turning around.

(Traditional, England)

Gobble-Gobble Rap

Me do a whispa and a big shout

with a meat-and-a-sweet mouth

like a non-meat, non-fish, puddn mouth

which is — a sleeper-waker, want-it-want-it mouth

which is — a take-it, break-it, eater mouth

which is — a gobble-gobble mouth.

Me do a whispa and a big shout

with an oily-oily, salty-pepper mouth

like any seafood, wing-food, ground-food mouth

which is — a want-more-now, want-more-now mouth

which is — a chopper-chopper, swallow-down mouth

which is — a gobble-gobble mouth.

 Me do a whispa and a big shout

with a boney-and-a-fleshy meaty mouth

like a buttered-up, creamed-up, oiled-up mouth

which is — a smile-and-smile, fries-and-fish mouth

which is — a loud, bossy-bossy mouth

which is — a gobble-gobble mouth.

Me do a whispa and a big shout
with a bun-and-cake and ice cream mouth
like shopping for a cupboard mouth
which is — a mouthy, eat-eat, noisy mouth
which is — a break-it-up, bite-it-up mouth
which is — a gobble-gobble mouth.

Me do a whispa and a big shout
with a pie, chocolate and apple mouth
like any chatty-chatty, suck-sweet mouth
which is — a on-and-off, laugh-and-laugh mouth
which is — a gimme-gimme-more mouth
which is — a gobble-gobble mouth.

Me do a whispa and a big shout
with always that ready mouth about
like even that slurper-burper mouth
which is — a raver-craver, seeker mouth
which is — a singer and kissy-kissy mouth
which is — a gobble-gobble mouth
which is — a gobble-gobble mouth.

James Berry (Jamaica/England)

What is the sound
of one hand clapping?

*This is a Japanese Koan. Koans show us that not everything
can be solved by logic and that some things can become a
riddling doorway to enlightenment.*

In the Jungle Restaurant

In among the green leaves,

Among the dangling vines,

All the hungry creatures

Were sitting down to dine.

"Lucy's juicy,"

said the tiger,

"Hughie's chewy,"

said the lion,

"Billy's chilly,"

said the panther,

"Won't you have a bit of mine?"

"Peter's pickled,"

said the rhino,

"Mary's hairy,"

said the shark,

"Andy's dandy,"

said the vulture,

"I found him in the park."

"Freddie's ready,"

said the python,

"Daphne's dainty,"

said the fox,

"Rita's sweeter,"

said the cheetah,

"I stole her off the ox."

"Chloe's doughy,"

said the raven,

"Sally's salty,"

said the bear.

"Sammy's tasteless,"

said the hippo,

"But I really don't care."

"Ron's all gone,"

burped the wild pig,

"Except for the very ends.

But I'm still a little hungry —

Had he any friends?"

Brian Patten (England)

The Uncertainty Of The Poet

I am a poet.

I am very fond of bananas.

I am bananas.

I am very fond of a poet.

I am a poet of bananas.

I am very fond.

A fond poet of "I am, I am" —

Very bananas.

Fond of "Am I bananas?

Am I" — a very poet.

Bananas of a poet!

Am I fond? Am I very?

Poet bananas! I am,

I am fond of a "very".

I am of very fond bananas.

Am I a poet?

Wendy Cope (England)

A Fat Poem

Fat is as fat is as fat is
Fat does as fat thinks

Fat feels
As fat please

Fat believes

    Fat is to butter

    As milk is to cream

    Fat is to sugar

    As pud is to steam

Fat is a dream
In times of lean

    Fat is a darling

    A dumpling

    A squeeze

    Fat is cuddles up a baby's sleeve

And fat speaks for itself

Grace Nichols (Guyana/England)

A Gallows Child's Calendar

Jaguary

Zebruary

Moose

Apeman

Margay

Coon

Shoofly

Aurochs

Sepiabear

Overbear

Novabear

Dinobear.

Christian Morgenstern (Germany)
Translated by **Anthea Bell**

THE FENCE

THERE WAS A FENCE WITH SPACE BETWEEN
THE PLANKS, SO YOU COULD SEE RIGHT IN.

AN ARCHITECT CAME BY ONE DAY
AND STOLE ALL THOSE SPACES AWAY.

HE TOOK THEM TO A BUILDING SITE
TO BUILD A HOUSE TWO FLOORS IN HEIGHT.

THE FENCE WAS LEFT THERE WILLY-NILLY:
A FENCE WITHOUT A SPACE LOOKS SILLY.

IT WAS AN EYESORE IN THE LAND.
THE STATE CONDEMNED IT OUT OF HAND.

AS FOR THE THIEF, HE GOT AWAY
TO AFRIC — OR AMERICAY!

Christian Morgenstern (Germany)
Translated by **Anthea Bell**

Weatherbee's Diner

When you're looking for something to eat

Weatherbee's Diner is just down the street.

Start off your meal with a bottle of rain.

Fog in the glass is imported from Maine.

The thunder is good, order it loud

with sundried tornado on top of a cloud.

Snow Flurry Curry is also a treat.

It's loaded with lightning and slathered in sleet.

Cyclones with hailstones are good for dessert,

but only have one or your belly will hurt.

Regardless of whether it's chilly or warm,

at Weatherbee's Diner they cook up a storm.

Calef Brown (USA)

My Sister

My sister's remarkably light,
She can float to a fabulous height.
It's a troublesome thing,
But we tie her with string,
And we use her instead of a kite.

Margaret Mahy (New Zealand)

The Cobra's Crimbo

A cobra once at Christmastime
(His name was Jim or Jimbo)
Lay sleeping, coiled, beside his wife
Who sat with coils akimbo.

Then he awoke and cried, "Alas!
I'm lost in mental limbo."
"I wish I was a poet like
My old mate Arthur Rimbo."

"Then I'd have words to wish for you
A truly Happy Crimbo."
His wife unforked her tongue and smiled.
"My slithery and slim beau!"

"You just have done, my darling one,
So don't be such a dimbo!"
"And New Year too," the cobra said,
And whizzed off up the chimbo.

Kit Wright (England)

The Frog

What a wonderful bird the frog are —

When he stand he sit almost;

When he hop, he fly almost;

He ain't got no sense hardly;

He ain't got no tail hardly either;

When he sit, he sit on what he ain't got almost.

(Traditional, USA)

"I am interested only in 'nonsense' only in that which makes no practical sense. I am interested in life only in its absurd manifestation."

Daniil Kharms

Daniil Kharms' name was Daniil Ivanovich Yuvachev but he took the name Kharms because of his fascination with the sounds of English words. It is believed that he made it up out of "charm" and "harm".

The Red-Haired Man

There was a red-haired man who had no eyes or ears.

Neither did he have any hair; he was called red-haired theoretically.

He couldn't speak, since he didn't have a mouth.

Neither did he have a nose.

He didn't even have any arms or legs. He had no stomach

and he had no back and he had no spine and he had no innards

whatsoever. He had nothing at all!

Therefore there's no knowing whom we are talking about.

In fact it's better that we don't say any more about him.

Daniil Kharms (Russia)
Translated by **Neil Cornwell**

Borderline Case

"You're a borderlinecase,"
They said to my face.
"A borderlinecase?"
I sighed in disgrace.
"Yes, borderlinecase —
Get out of this place."

So I went to the border,
Still not knowing
If I was coming
Or if I was going.
And I found the border
And stood on the line,
But nobody wanted
A case like mine.

"THERE IS MUCH NONSENSE IN
PLATYPUS, A CREATURE
JABBERWOCKY FOR
colin

For "No" said the left camp

And "No" said the right.

(For a borderlinecase is

An unwelcome sight.)

Then I could see

Some other sorts

Who looked like me.

So I went to them,

And the smile on their faces

Told me that here was

The best of all places,

Amongst all the other

Borderlinecases.

Colin West (England)

NATURE. TAKE THE DUCKBILLED
WHICH RIVALS THE
SHEER OUTLANDISHNESS."
West

Pumpkin-Grumpkin

(If) Pumpkin-Grumpkin dances —
Don't, for heaven's sake, go where the stable horse prances;
Don't look left, don't look right, don't take no silly chances.
Instead, cling with all four legs to the holler-radish branches.

(If) Pumpkin-Grumpkin cries —
Beware! Beware! Don't sit on rooftops high up in the skies;
Crouch down low on a machan bundled to the eyes,
Sing "Radhe Krishno Radhe" till your lusty throat dries.

(If) Pumpkin-Grumpkin laughs —
Stand next to the kitchen poised on straight and skinny calves;
Speak Persian in a misty voice and breathe through silken scarves;
Sleep on the grass, skip all three meals, no doing things by halves!

(If) Pumpkin-Grumpkin runs —
Make sure you scramble up the windows all at once;
Mix rouge with hookah water and on your face smear tons;
And don't dare look up at the sky thinking you're great guns!

(If) Pumpkin-Grumpkin calls —

Clap legal hats on to your heads, float in basins down the halls;

Pound spinach into healing paste and smear your forehead walls;

And with a red-hot pumice stone rub your nose until it crawls.

Those of you who find this foolish and dare to laugh it off,

When Pumpkin-Grumpkin gets to know, you won't want to scoff.

Then you'll see which words of mine are full of truth and how.

Don't come running to me then, I'm telling you right now.

Sukumar Ray (India)
Translated by **Sampurna Chattarji**

*Sukumar Ray (1887–1923) was a Bengali illustrator and
writer of nonsense verse. He even founded the Nonsense
Club soon after leaving college. Here's what his son,
Satyajit Ray, the famous filmmaker, says about his Dad's
kind of nonsense: "Sukumar named this special vein of
nonsense the Rasa, or 'spirit of whimsy'. Needless to say, it
is not one of the nine Rasas of Indian dramatic theory."*

Edward Lear

How lovely to meet Edward Lear
Whose heart held nonsense dear!
For in nonsense, pure and absolute,
he found the fleetoobious truth.
And many a word from Hindustan
he embraced with his limerick hand.
And so by nonsensical decree,
an AYAH, the Hindi for NANNY,
perches on the tallest tree.
And DOBIE, a WASHERMAN,
dares to sit as only a cushion can.
And a JAMPAN, meaning SEDAN CHAIR,
howls from its lupustrious lair.
How lovely to meet Edward Lear!

John Agard (Guyana/England)

The Cummerbund

An Indian Poem

I

She sat upon her Dobie,

To watch the Evening Star,

And all the Punkahs as they passed

Cried, "My! how fair you are!"

Around her bower, with quivering leaves,

The tall Kamsamahs grew,

And Kitmutgars in wild festoons

Hung down from Tchokis blue.

II

Below her home the river rolled

With soft meloobious sound,

Where golden-finned Chuprassies swam,

In myriads circling round.

Above, on tallest trees remote,

Green Ayahs perched alone,

And all night long the Mussak moaned

Its melancholy tone.

III

And where purple Nullahs threw
Their branches far and wide,
And silvery Goreewallahs flew
In silence, side by side,
The little Bheesties' twittering cry
Rose on the fragrant air,
And oft the angry Jampan howled
Deep in his hateful lair.

IV

She sat upon her Dobie,
She heard the Nimmak hum,
When all at once a cry arose:
"The Cummerbund is come!"
In vain she fled — with open jaws
The angry monster followed,
And so (before assistance came),
That Lady Fair was swallowed.

V

They sought in vain for even a bone

Respectfully to bury;

They said, "Hers was a dreadful fate!"

(And Echo answered, "Very.")

They nailed her Dobie to the wall,

Where last her form was seen,

And underneath they wrote these words,

In yellow, blue, and green:

"Beware, ye Fair! Ye Fair, beware!

Nor sit out late at night,

Lest horrid Cummerbunds should come,

And swallow you outright."

Edward Lear (England)

Limericks before Lear

A merry old man of Oporto,
Had long had the gout in his fore toe;
 And oft when he spoke
 To relate a good joke
A terrible twinge cut it short O!

There was a sick man of Tobago
Liv'd long on rice-gruel and sago;
 But at last to his bliss
The physician said this —
"To a roast leg of mutton you may go."

Richard Scrafton Sharpe (England)

Limericks by Lear

There was an Old Man who, when little,
Fell casually into a kettle;
　　But growing too stout
　　He could never get out —
So he passed all his life in that kettle!

There was an Old Person of Ware,
Who rode on the back of a bear.
　　When asked, "Does it trot?"
　　He said, "Certainly not!
He's a Moppsikon Floppsikon bear!"

Edward Lear (England)

Limericks after Lear

A High that was learning to Low

Met a Stop that was learning to Go.

They walked hand in hand

Till they came to a land

Of a Yes that was learning to No.

Willard R. Espy (USA)

A sumo wrestler chappy

One day in the ring was unhappy.

When thrown to the ground

His mum pinned him down

And in view of the crowd changed his nappy.

Paul Cookson (England)

Jeremy, Jeremy Bishop,

Was a good boy, he ate all his fishop.

When he was done,

Like a well-brought up son,

He washed and dried his dishop.

Valerie Bloom (Jamaica/England)

A tutor who tooted the flute
Tried to tutor two tooters to toot.
　　Said the two to the tutor,
　　"Is it harder to toot or
To tutor two tooters to toot?"

Carolyn Wells (USA)

A football fanatic in strife
Found telly had altered his life.
Now his eyes are quite square
With a switch in his hair
And he's turned on and off by his wife.

Max Fatchen (Australia)

"To appreciate nonsense requires a serious interest in life."
Gelett Burgess

The Floorless Room

I wish that my room had a floor!
I don't so much care for a door.
But this crawling around
Without touching the ground
Is getting to be quite a bore.

Gelett Burgess (USA)

My TV Came Down with a Chill

My TV came down with a chill.

As soon as I saw it was ill

I wrapped up its channels

In warm winter flannels

And gave its antenna a pill.

Willard R. Espy (USA)

The Computer's First Christmas Card

jollymerry

hollyberry

jollyberry

merryholly

happyjolly

jollyjelly

jellybelly

bellymerry

hollyheppy

jollyMolly

marryJerry

merryHarry

hoppyBarry

heppyJarry

boppyheppy

berryjorry

jorryjolly

moppyjelly

Mollymerry

Jerryjolly

bellyboppy

jorryhoppy

hollymoppy

Barrymerry

Jarryhappy

happyboppy

boppyjolly

jollymerry

merrymerry

merrymerry

merryChris

ammerryasa

Chrismerry

asMERRYCHR

YSANTHEMUM

Edwin Morgan (Scotland)

The Computer's First Proverbs

An improvisation on the *Oxford Dictionary of Proverbs*

After Edwin Morgan

You can take a dog to the keyside,

but you can't push him in

all is wet that starts to bark

if you pay peanuts you get them planted in the park

nothing should be done in haste but grip your trout

if you want fish, you must prepare for stink

he who fishes with the piper barks like a dog

he who fishes a tiger is afraid to wink

fish will out, fish will out

all roaring is the same in the dark.

A dog in the brook is worth avoiding

think of a fountain and you froth in the head

speech is water, fish are water

it is too late to rub in embrocation

after the dream has gone

strike while the law is out

put the stout dog to a deaf oven

flush the fridge if you have a long arm

idle lips make the best smoke rings

fishmongers always make room

it is all melted that ends melted

in May let the plugs bloom

you cannot roar with the workers

and ignore the phone

it takes three waders to make a wet man

the longest dog winks all the way home

Peter Finch (Wales)

Eletelephony

Once there was an elephant,
Who tried to use the telephant —
No! No! I mean an elephone
Who tried to use the telephone —
(Dear me! I am not certain quite
That even now I've got it right.)

Howe'er it was, he got his trunk
Entangled in the telephunk;
The more he tried to get it free,
The louder buzzed the telephee —
(I fear I'd better drop the song
Of elephop and telephong!)

Laura Richards (USA)

Invaders

Celts wore kilts,

Romans had omens,

The Vikings had a liking for hiking.

Goths wore cloths,

Moguls were scared of bogles,

Vandals strolled in sandals.

Anglo-Saxons put their Ankle-Soxon.

John Rice (Scotland)

All the Things You Can Say to Places in the UK

Always say "Ta" to Leamington Spa,

say "Have a nice day" to Whitley Bay.

You can shout "What's new" or even "Howdoo"

to inhabitants of Looe or Crewe.

You can tell the whole story in Tobermory,

say "Hi" to Rye and "Right on" to Brighton,

or call out "Let's go" to Plymouth Ho.

Talk through your dreams in Milton Keynes,

say "It's all for the best" in Haverfordwest.

Always say "Yes" when you visit Skegness

but only say "No" in Llandudno.

Don't tell a lie to the Island of Skye

or say "It smells" in Tunbridge Wells.

Don't talk rude if you're down in Bude

or start to get gabby in Waltham Abbey.

Don't ever plead in Berwick on Tweed

or say "You look ill" to Burgess Hill.

You could lose your voice and talk with your hands

when you take a trip to Camber Sands,

but whatever you say just won't impress

the residents of Shoeburyness.

Brian Moses (Engand)

The Howdooyoodoo

Haven't you heard
of the Howdooyoodoo
Howdooyoodoo?

I'm surprised
you haven't heard
of the Howdooyoodoo
Howdooyoodoo

Spend a day or two
in a place called England
and I'm sure you'll meet
the Howdooyoodoo
Howdooyoodoo

But for those of you
without a clue
the Howdooyoodoo
is a creeping kind of plant
that takes you by the hand
and says Howdooyoodoo
Howdooyoodoo

And if by chance
you should say
I'm feeling down today
I got a pain in my brain
And me eyes keep spilling
drops of rain
that doctors can't restrain

Then the Howdooyoodoo
gets embarrassed
almost a fright
Retreats into itself
and begins to wither

So upon meeting
the Howdooyoodoo
this most peculiar plant
Don't be alarmed
Be polite
Just take it by the hand
And say Howdooyoodoo
Howdooyoodoo
Howdooyoodoooooooooooooo

John Agard (Guyana/ England)

A Sense-less Poem

I'm having trouble with my ears —
They do not see so well.
My eyes are also failing fast —
They've lost their sense of smell.
My nose has lost its power of speech,
My tongue, its sense of touch.
Alas, your sympathy's in vain —
My hands can't hear you much.

Carey Blyton (England)

When Fishes Set Umbrellas Up

When fishes set umbrellas up
    If the rain-drops run,
Lizards will want their parasols
    To shade them from the sun.

The peacock has a score of eyes,
    With which he cannot see;
The cod-fish has a silent sound,
    However that may be.

No dandelions tell the time
    Although they turn to clocks;
Cat's cradle does not hold the cat,
    Nor foxglove fit the fox.

Christina Rossetti (England)

Rhymes

Two respectable rhymes
skipped out of their pages
like two proud roosters
from golden cages.

They walked many a mile
in search of a home,
but could find no space
for themselves in a poem.

They grew tired and sad
but wherever they went
nobody advertised
poems for rent.

People whispered and said:
haven't you heard
that a rhyming word
is considered absurd?

In modern times
who needs rhymes?
Those high-flying words
went out with the birds.

At last one night
all weary and worn
they came to a house
in a field of corn.

And there lived a man
who still wrote lines
according to rules
from olden times.

So he took them in
with doubles and pairs,
and set them to music,
and gave them new airs.

Now they ring again
their bells and chimes,
and the children all sing
those respectable rhymes.

With one rhyme inside
and another one out:
the rhymes were befriended
and my poem is ended.

J. I. Segal (Canada)
Translated from Yiddish by **Miriam Waddington**

The Maple Leaves that Mable Leaves

Mable leaves
the maple leaves
she's raking in a pile

to make believe
she's Cleopatra
sailing up the Nile.

You may believe
the maple leaves
that Mable leaves
are make believe

But I believe
the maple leaves
that Mable leaves
are real.

And ever since she ran from them
I've been the one who's raking them —
I can't believe that you believe that
I would dream of faking them.

So maybe leave
what you believe
out of this entirely

and imagine for a moment
how badly I must feel

that you believe
the maple leaves
that Mable leaves

aren't real.

JonArno Lawson (Canada)

"Trying to make
Sense of
nonsense
brings us back
to our senses."
JonArno Lawson

Mulla Nasruddin

Nasruddin was throwing handfuls
of bread all around his house.

"What are you doing?" someone asked.

"Keeping the tigers away."

"But there are no tigers around here."

"Exactly. Effective, isn't it?"

Traditional (Middle East)

Mulla Nasruddin

One day, Nasruddin went through the streets of Aksehir

Dancing and singing and laughing out loud.

"Why are you so happy?" the people asked.

"Ah, my friends, my donkey is missing!"

"But, Hodja, is that any reason to be happy?"

"But of course, my friends!

After all, if I had been sitting on it,

I'd be missing too!"

Traditional (Middle East)

It is believed that Mulla Nasruddin's origin goes back over 800 years to Turkey, where he is known as Mulla Khodja. But whether Nasruddin or simply Mulla, he is a popular figure in the wisdom stories of the Middle East and Central Asia. Mulla's "nonsense logic" often disguises seeds of truth. Would you call him "a wise fool" or "a foolish wise man"?

Seasick

"I don't feel whelk," whaled the squid, sole-fully.

"What's up?" asked the doctopus.

"I've got sore mussels and a tunny-hake," she told him.

"Lie down and I'll egg salmon you," mermaid the doctopus.

"Rays your voice," said the squid. "I'm a bit hard of herring."

"Sorry! I didn't do it on porpoise,"
replied the doctopus orc-wardly.

He helped her to oyster self onto his couch

And asked her to look up so he could sea urchin.

He soon flounder plaice that hurt.

"This'll make it eel," he said, whiting a prescription.

"So I won't need to see the sturgeon?" she asked.

"Oh, no," he told her. "In a couple of dace you'll feel brill."

"Cod bless you," she said.

"That'll be sick squid," replied the doctopus.

Nick Toczek (England)

Mad Weather We're Having

It's raining cats and dogs again,
It said so on the news.
Last Sunday it rained penguins,
On Monday, kangaroos.

On Tuesday, it was froggy,
On Wednesday, cold as mice,
On Thursday, it snowed polar bears
(which wasn't very nice).

Friday was a fowl day,
Saturday was bats,
And now we're back to Sunday
With a load more dogs and cats.

I'd like to stay here talking
But I'm soaking to the skin.
Now it's blowing up a buffalo
I think I'm going in.

Kaye Umansky (England)

Advice to a Young Ghost

"Please remember,
Whatever you do
Don't spook until
You're spooken to."

Trevor Harvey (England)

Crooked Song

I went into a crooked bush

And cut a crooked stick,

I stuck it by a crooked yam

And took a crooked hoe.

I dug the crooked yam again

And gave it to a crooked girl,

Who cooked it on a crooked fire

And gave it to a crooked man,

Who ate the crooked yam.

(Traditional, Nigeria)

A Man With a Hat On

A man with a hat on, I say no:
How should I know he is bald,
Bald, bald, nothing but bald,
Yes, indeed, nothing but bald?

A man with trousers on, I say no:
How should I know he is bow-legged,
Bow-legged, bow-legged, nothing but bow-legged,
Yes, indeed, nothing but bow-legged?

A man with glasses on, I say no:
How should I know he has a squint,
A squint, a squint, nothing but a squint,
Yes, indeed, nothing but a squint?

A man with shoes on, I say no:
How should I know his toes have jiggers,
Jiggers, jiggers, nothing but jiggers,
Yes, indeed, nothing but jiggers?

Anon (Malawi)

Spring Song

Archibald Spratt
wore a cat for a hat
which he stuck to his head with glue;
on the first day of spring
he would walk round in rings
shouting, "God Save the King"
WHAT'S NEW?

Marjorie Sugg
cleaned her teeth with a slug
that was taped to the end of a screw;
on the first day of spring
she would sprout lovely wings
and fly off to Beijing
WHAT'S NEW?

Otto van Krantz

kept red ants in his pants

and fed them with apples and stew;

on the first day of spring

he would buy lots of string

and tie it round things

WHAT'S NEW?

The first day of spring,

oh, the first day of spring,

there's no day more wondrous, it's true;

when that sparky mad zing

hits you like a bee sting

there's no choice but to sing

hello halloo!

and go totally cuckoo

WHAT'S NEW?

Mark C. Hewitt (England)

O'er Seas That Have No Beaches

O'er seas that have no beaches

To end their waves upon,

I floated with twelve peaches,

A sofa and a swan.

The blunt waves crashed above us

The sharp waves burst around,

There was no one to love us,

No hope of being found —

Where, on the notched horizon

So endlessly a-drip,

I saw all of a sudden

No sign of any ship.

Mervyn Peake (England)

Hypothesis

If a shark
could bark

If an owl
could howl

If a cow
could meow

If a fawn
could yawn

If a boar
could roar

If the bees
could sneeze

Dear readers, I apologize
But sometimes, I zoologize.

Nina Cassian (Romania)

The Ant

An ant of eighteen metres

And on his head a hat.

That cannot be, that cannot be.

An ant pulling a cartload,

penguins and ducks aboard.

That cannot be, that cannot be.

An ant speaking french, if you please

Speaking latin and javanese.

That cannot be, that cannot be.

    Eh! Why not!

Robert Desnos (France)
Translated by **John Agard**

The Agnostic Shrimp

Said the big shrimp to the cuttlefish

    You may think it's odd

I'm a prawn-again crustacean

    But I don't believe in cod.

Roger Stevens (England)

HUMPTY DUMPTY

(from **Through the Looking Glass**)

"You seem very clever at explaining words, Sir," said Alice. "Would you kindly tell me the meaning of the poem called 'Jabberwocky'?"

"Let's hear it," said Humpty Dumpty. "I can explain all the poems that ever were invented — and a good many that haven't been invented just yet."

This sounded very helpful, so Alice repeated the first verse:

"'Twas brillig, and the slithy toves
Did gyre and gimble in the wabe:
All mimsy were the borogoves,
And the mome raths outgrabe."

"That's enough to begin with," Humpty Dumpty interrupted: "there are plenty of hard words there. 'Brillig' means four o'clock in the afternoon — the time when you begin broiling things for dinner."

"That'll do very well," said Alice: "and 'slithy'?"

"Well, 'slithy' means 'lithe and slimy'" ...

"And what's to 'gyre' and to 'gimble'?"

"To 'gyre' is to go round and round like a gyroscope. To 'gimble' is to make holes like a gimblet."

Lewis Carroll (England)

Jabberwocky

'Twas brillig, and the slithy toves
    Did gyre and gimble in the wabe;
All mimsy were the borogoves,
    And the mome raths outgrabe.

"Beware the Jabberwock, my son!
    The jaws that bite, the claws that catch!
Beware the Jubjub bird, and shun
    The frumious Bandersnatch!"

He took his vorpal sword in hand:
    Long time the manxome foe he sought —
So rested he by the Tumtum tree,
    And stood awhile in thought.

And, as in uffish thought he stood,
    The Jabberwock, with eyes of flame,
Came whiffling through the tulgey wood,
    And burbled as it came!

One, two! One, two! And through and through
    The vorpal blade went snicker-snack!
He left it dead, and with its head
    He went galumphing back.

"And hast thou slain the Jabberwock?
    Come to my arms, my beamish boy!
Oh frabjous day! Callooh! Callay!"
    He chortled in his joy.

'Twas brillig, and the slithy toves
    Did gyre and gimble in the wabe;
All mimsy were the borogoves,
    And the mome raths outgrabe.

Lewis Carroll (England)

"Why is A Raven Like A Writing Desk?"
Lewis Carroll

Some say this question has no answer at all and was just a Mad Hatter mind game from the nonsense writer/ mathematician Lewis Carroll (1832-1898) of **Alice in Wonderland** *fame.*

Some say the answer is: "Because Edgar Allan Poe wrote on both," referring to the fact that Poe wrote a famous poem about a raven and might well have written it on a writing desk!

Some say the answer is, "Because they both come with inky quills," referring to the fact that long ago writing desks came with inkwells and feather pens.

Who knows?

The Quest Of The Deep-Freeze Knight

My armour is wafers
My helmet's a cone
As I fearlessly march
Through the Ice-Cream Zone

I journey on
Towards my duty
Through the bright Forest
Of Tutti Frutti

Past Strawberry Hill
And Vanilla-Tree
I keep my mind chill
And military

Then under a bush
Of Pistachios
I trim my ferocious
Moustachios

Then I don silver boots
And onwards I trudge
Over the Desert
Of Chocolate Fudge

Will I see
From some far and fatal ridge —
Cassata Castle
And the King of the Fridge?

Adrian Mitchell (England)

The Emergensea

The octopus awoke one morning and wondered
What rhyme it was.
Looking at his alarm-clocktopus
He saw that it had stopped
And it was time to stop having a rest
And get himself dressed.
On every octofoot
He put
An octosocktopus
But in his hurry, one foot got put
Not into an octosocktopus
But into an electric plug socket
And the octopus got a nasty electric shocktopus
And had to call the octodoctopus
Who couldn't get in
To give any help or medicine
Because the door was loctopus.
The octopus couldn't move,
Being in a state of octoshocktopus
So the octodoctopus bashed the door
To the floor
And the cure was as simple as could be:
A nice refreshing cup of seawater.

John Hegley (England)

Out In the Desert

Out in the desert lies the Sphinx

It never eats and it never drinx

Its body's quite solid without any chinx

And when the sky's all purple and pinx

(As if it was painted with coloured inx)

And the sun it ever so swiftly sinx

Behind the hills in a couple of twinx

You may hear (if you're lucky) a bell that clinx

And also tolls and also tinx

And they say at the very same sound the Sphinx

It sometimes smiles and it sometimes winx

But nobody knows just what it thinx

Charles Causley (England)

Epitaph for Humpty Dumpty

Beneath this wall there lies the shell

Of someone who had talents.

But (as you can probably tell)

One of them wasn't balance.

Rachel Rooney (England)

In Memory of Fido

Here lies Fido, Oh the Grief,

How we will miss his gnashing teeth,

Thief of all our Sunday roasts,

Pray that he's now biting ghosts!

Andrew Fusek Peters (England)

Epitaph

Here lies Dracula.

He's either on his backula

Or standing right behind you

Getting ready to attackula.

Kaye Umansky (England)

Rhyme-osaur the Dinosaur

Out of a deep dark mine-osaur

at roughly half past nine-osaur

there came a sleepy steg-osaur

into the warm sunshine-osaur

he warmed his chilly spine-osaur

which made him feel divine-osaur

he nibbled on a pine-osaur

and drank a glass of wine-osaur

but then he saw a sign-osaur

which made him yelp and whine-osaur

it forecast his decline-osaur

his time had come to die-nosaur

John Rice (Scotland)

No Peas for the Wicked

No peas for the wicked
No carrots for the damned
No parsnips for the naughty
   O Lord we pray

No sprouts for the shameless
No cabbage for the shady
No lettuce for the lecherous
   No way, no way

No potatoes for the deviants
No radish for the riff-raff
No spinach for the spineless
   Lock them away

No beetroot for the boasters
No mange-tout for the mobsters
No corn-on-the-cob etcetera
   (Shall we call it a day?)

Roger McGough (England)

from "Excuse me, is this India?"

I hopped into a three-wheeled car
And called out "Take me there!"
The driver started off at once,
He never asked me "Where?"

Suddenly he stopped and said,
"At last we're getting near."
"Near to what?" I asked him.
He bellowed in my ear:
"Near to this is far from that!
I think that's very clear!"

Though it wasn't clear to me,
I nodded very cleverly.

At a shop I stopped to see
If I could get a hint
Of where I was, but all I saw
Were clothes of every tint.
"Where am I and what's this place?"
I asked of everyone.
A woman came and said to me,
"You're as far as you can run.

But if you learn to fly, then you
Could catch up with the sun."

I left the shop
With a happy hop.

I hopped until the airport
And there! There was a sign.
But suddenly I realized
I couldn't read a line.

I asked a bearded gentleman.
He said, "Oh don't you know?
It doesn't matter where you are
But where you want to go."

Anushka Ravishankar (India)

"I'm a great fan of Lewis Carroll's nonsense. Like Carroll, I studied mathematics, so I have a special affinity for logic, and by extension, illogical nonsense. Nonsense lets you jump out of the boundaries of language and logic."

Anushka Ravishankar

The Samosa Feud

There is an old feud that needs to be settled —
Call a "samosa" a "shingara"
   and the Punjabi gets nettled.
Call a "shingara" a "samosa"
   and the Bengali gets mad,
While the two are fighting,
   there's a plateful to be had.

Sampurna Chattarji (India)

Frankie

I

I love Frankie, you love Frankie
Obviously there's some hanky-panky.

II

Frankie's not a little boy
who lives down the lane.
He's a fat and juicy roll
with a kebab for a brain.

Sampurna Chattarji (India)

"To me, nonsense is a game we play in which humour and insight, imagination and anarchy bounce in amazing (and amazingly rigorous) patterns on the trampoline of language."

Sampurna Chattarji

Ten Things You Should Know About Hippopotamuses

1. What is a young female hippopotamus called?

   A hippopotamiss.

2. What do parents say to a young hippo
   when telling him not to do something?

   A hippopotamusn't.

3. How do you train a baby hippopotamus?

   By sitting him on a hippopotty.

4. What does a hippo like spread on his burgers?

   Lots of hippopotamustard.

5. What kind of dance music
   does a hippopotamus like?

   Hip-hop.

6. What do you call a hippopotamus who says
   things behind other hippopotamuses' backs?

   A hippo-crit.

7. What do you call a hippopotamus
with chicken pox?

   A hippospotamus.

8. What do you call a hippopotamus with a limp?

   A hoppopotamus.

9. What do hippopotamuses shout
when they're cheering somebody?

   Hip! Hip! Hooray!

10. What do you call a hippopotamus
with a smile on its face?

    A happypotamus.

John Foster (England)

Something to Worry About

Nothing rhymes wid **nothing**
I discovered dat today
Now I hav two more words
To help me rhyme away,
Nothing + **nothing** = **nothing**
I am good at maths as well
I feel like a professor
As me head begins to swell.

If I start wid **nothing**
I hav **nothing** to lose
And now dat I hav two **nothings**
It's easier to choose,
Nothing gets me worried
I hope you overstand
I am now enjoying **nothing**
And I hav **nothing** planned.

I am busy doing **nothing**

Me parents think it's great

I am in luv wid **nothing**

And there's **nothing** dat I hate,

I will give you **nothing**

So you hav **nothing** to fear

Let me tell you **nothing**

I hav **nothing** to declare.

Nothing's rong wid **nothing**

It's such a great idea

It need not be created

I hav **nothing** to share,

Nothing rhymes wid **nothing**

There waz **nothing** at de start

And I can't give you anything

When there's **nothing** in my heart.

Benjamin Zephaniah (England)

Whatnot

There's a shop in the High Street that deals in antiques,
And I've looked in the window for weeks and for weeks,
But I've not yet been able to understand why
The price of a Whatnot should be quite so high.

A Thingumabob wouldn't be such a price,
A What-you-may-call-it would look just as nice,
But neither of these things would cost half as much,
And you buy them in shops
where you're welcome to touch.

An Oojamaflip is as rare and as big,
And so for that matter's a Thingumajig,
But neither of these is expensive to buy,
So why is the price of a Whatnot so high?

Colin West (England)

Logic

A girl said:
"I wrote myself a letter."
So I said:
"What did it say?"
She said:
"I don't know.
I won't get it till tomorrow."

A boy said:
"I'm really glad my mum called me Jack."
I said:
"Why's that?"
He said:
"Because all the kids at school
call me that."

Michael Rosen (England)

At The Vegetable Stall

At the vegetable stall on market day,
Such conversations are the way:
"You may lean on me, Mr Dill,
You really have gone through the mill."
"Now is that surprising, my dear Chive?
I've been withering here since five!"
Then to that Kohlrabi says:
"Just look at robust Turnip's rays!"
Pea moves to pat Turnip's blushes,
And to ask: "No more crushes?"
"Thank you, no. Hardly at all,
That's to say, since the last fall."
"But Miss Parsnip is so poorly,
Pale, thin, and quite deadly, really."
"Oh, what a life!"
Sighed Old Knife.
Mr Beetroot keeps his distance,
From Miss Onion's dire insistence:
"My dear Beetroot, my red darling,
Will you not be my Prince Charming?"

Mr Beetroot only holds his breath:

"Away you go, not for all the world's wealth.

I want a dear beetroot wife,

Without days of crying strife."

"Oh, what a life!"

Sighed Old Knife.

Then quite suddenly Bean was heard:

"And you also want to join the herd?"

"Don't be too big for your boots."

To this little Brussels Sprout hoots.

"Did you ever see the like?"

Bristled Carrot at the fight.

"Let's ask Cabbage for some help."

"Cabbage! That head's soft as felt!"

To that Cabbage asks them sadly:

"Why are you quibbling so madly?

Why the stupid altercation

When soup is our destination?"

"Oh, what a life!"

Sighed Old Knife.

Jan Brzechwa (Poland)
Translated by **Aniela Korzeniowska**

Hoopoe's Nothing Song

Nobody nothing
anyone anything
none with nothing —
never.

Nobody nothing
anyone anything
no nothing —
empty-handed.

Anything to any
nothing nothing
no nothing —
not for nothing.

Marcelijus Martinaitis (Lithuania)

The Bluebillgurgle

I am the bluebillgurgle,
My father was a purgle,
My mother was a porulam,
There come weird children from.
Rabom, rabom, rabom.

I am the bluebillgurgle,
The only food I like is curgle,
Except when the night-owl cries.
Then I eat reep and rimmle-rice.
Rabice, rabice, rabice.

I am the bluebillgurgle,
When I don't wock or wurgle,
I'm lying basking in the sun,
And cnooster with my czezidun,
Rabun, rabun, rabun.

I am the bluebillgurgle,
Once I shall die of scurgle,
Change shrinking as a crix I shall,
Into a nice blue pebble, rounded well,
To hell, to hell, to hell!

Cees Buddingh' (Holland)
Translated by **James Holmes**

Hocus-Pocus

A hunter shot a coconut

(a hocus-pocus coconut)

which fell upon a legionnaire

and tousled up his hat and hair.

He used it as a cannon ball

and hit an animal so tall

it must have been a great giraffe,

who swallowed it and gave a laugh,

then spat it out so high it fell

upon the hunter's head. Farewell!

Poor hunter, powdered in a wink

to hocus-pocus cocoa drink.

Halfdan Rasmussen (Denmark)
Translated by **Glyn W. Jones**

Froots and Vegedibles

In the froot department the choices impress
but it's the delicacies that I like best.
There I find seafigs, grumpkins, superapples,
winberries, fairfruits, litrons, prattles.
Greenevers, flatberries, playsins,
and pinkishly dotted green straysins.
Boorerries, snowchewy grapes, daisyduckables,
Seasweet kneadles and bitter suckables.
Munchesters and grammophins,
queuesorrels and sproutuffins.
Soft vulcherries and mellowins,
cultured figs and keynotethinns.
Camelly kernels, prunegranates, elderries,
writeapples, movieberries and counseleries.
Witnuts, weaklings, adherries,
pseudopears and ecstaberries.
Candylimes, bristly chucknuts,
fleshfigs and guess-me-nots.
Excessseeds and argentinnies,
spinach ducks and superrappinis.

The eat-growth department is great,
so popular that I can hardly wait.
Boilonions, chatkale, hobby-chews,
new epickles and fresh pearmushroos.
Automatoes and frumpishes,
fur-beans, archturnips and tradishes.
Aromatoes and wishroot,
yellow excits and lettucefoot.
Blue-eyed peas, groantatoes, thymusthistles,
black choirblades and ediblistles.
Sanddales, moodroot and springwalktoes,
purring petleeks and adequatoes.
Cool boneradishes, beancucamberries,
breadroots and archichopcherries.
Tongue-lashings and porklamines,
savoyfears and apartgreens.
overripers and garlick cloves,
minionions and squirrelgloves.
It's good to eat vegedibles and froots,
People's disposition is better than good.
Digestion will be finer than fine.
And to a joyful poem the belly says goodbye.

Thórarinn Eldjárn (Iceland)
Translated by **Olga Holownia**

Great Cow Artists

PICOWSSO

MOONET

MICHELANGELOW

CONSTABLE

MOODIGLIANI

MOOTISSE

LEONARDO BAA VINCI (he was a sheep, actually)

EDVARD MOONCH (his most famous painting is *The Cream*)

OSCAR COWKOSCHKA

EL GRECOW

FRIDA COWLO.

Carol Ann Duffy (Scotland)

Best Friend

If my best friend was a cow,

her hide would feel like silk,

and she'd be full of lemonade,

not milk.

Her udders would be bagpipes,

they'd play a Scottish tune,

and we'd dance together,

two daft cows,

then jump right over the moon.

Carol Ann Duffy (Scotland)

Pig's Song of Courtship

Grobble Snort

Blurp Blort

Screep Uggle

Slop Snuffle

Honk Squelch

Flubber Belch

Wee — Say

Wee — You

Wee — Love

Wee — Me

John Mole (England)

Pig's Lullaby

Trouble Sorrow

Dropple Wallow

Snort Snorkle Deep

Sadly Sobble

Cradle Wobble

Sleep Sleep Sleep

John Mole (England)

Mornsong

Rise in the morning,
face the unknown.
Iron your skin
and polish your bone.

Eat up your breakfast
of pie in the sky.
Your thoughts are the best
that pennies can buy.

Clouds are like dripping
stuck to a bowl.
Rain is a mare
giving birth to a foal.

It's time you left home
for the front of the class.
The wider the mark,
the greater the gas.

Your school is a lab

where test tubes play pranks.

Your class is a form

where you fill in your blanks.

Pack a lunch of smoked apples

or cornflakes and fries.

Splash out on fresh rainshine,

yawn open your eyes.

Dennis O'Driscoll (Ireland)

Incantation by Laughter

O laugh it out, you laughsters!

O laugh it up, you laughsters!

So they laugh with laughters,

so they laugherize delaughly.

O laugh it up belaughably!

O the laughingstock of the laughed-upon —

the laugh of belaughed laughsters!

O laugh it out roundlaughingly,

the laugh of laughed-at laughians!

Laugherino, laugherino,

Laughify, laughicate, laugholets, laugholets,

Laughikins, laughikins,

O laugh it out, you laughsters!

O laugh it up, you laughsters!

Velimir Khlebnikov (Russia)
Translated by **Gary Kern**

INDEX OF POETS

Acknowledgements

SOUNDS OF ASIA copyright © Takashi Arima. From JOURNEY TO THE REAL published by Shambhala Publications. **HINDI CLASS** copyright © J.P. Das. Reproduced by permission of the author. **COATI-MUNDI** copyright © William Jay Smith. From LAUGHING TIME by William Jay Smith (Farrar Straus & Giroux, 1990). **UP FROM DOWN UNDER** copyright © David McCord, from TAKE SKY by David McCord (Little Brown, 1962). **TOO MANY DAVES** from THE SNEETCHES AND OTHER STORIES ™ & © 1961 Dr. Seuss Enterprises, L.P. Used by Permission. All rights reserved. **I SHALL TELL A SILLY TALE** copyright © Andrew Fusek Peters. Reproduced by permission of the author. **THE CARCAJOU AND THE KINCAJOU** copyright © 1957 Ogden Nash. Reprinted by permission of Curtis Brown, Ltd. **THE PUFFIN WHO LIVED IN A MUFFIN** copyright © Yansan Agard. Reproduced by permission of the author. **ON THE NING NANG NONG** copyright © Spike Milligan. Reproduced by permission of Spike Milligan Productions Ltd. **GOBBLE-GOBBLE RAP** copyright © 1988 James Berry, from WHEN I DANCE by James Berry. Reproduced by permission of PFD (www.pfd.co.uk) on behalf of James Berry. **IN THE JUNGLE RESTAURANT** copyright © Brian Patten. Reproduced by permission of the author c/o Rogers, Coleridge & White Ltd., 20 Powis Mews, London WII IJN. **THE UNCERTAINTY OF THE POET** copyright © Wendy Cope. **A FAT POEM** copyright © Grace Nichols, from A FAT BLACK WOMAN'S POEMS by Grace Nichols. Reproduced by permission of Virago Press, an imprint of Little, Brown Book Group. **A GALLOWS CHILD'S CALENDAR** from LULLABIES, LYRICS AND GALLOWS by Christian Morgenstern. Translated by Anthea Bell, illustrated by Lisbeth Zwerger. Copyright © 1992 by NordSüd Verlag AG, Zurich/Switzerland. All rights reserved. Published by arrangement with North-South Books Inc., New York. First published in Switzerland under the title Kindergedichte und Galgenlieder. English translation copyright © 1995 by North-South Books Inc., New York. **THE FENCE** from LULLABIES, LYRICS AND GALLOWS by Christian Morgenstern. Translated by Anthea Bell, illustrated by Lisbeth Zwerger. Copyright © 1992 by NordSüd Verlag AG, Zurich/Switzerland. All rights reserved. Published by arrangement with North-South Books Inc., New York. First published in Switzerland under the title Kindergedichte und Galgenlieder. English translation copyright © 1995 by North-South Books Inc., New York. **WEATHERBEE'S DINER** copyright © 2006 Calef Brown. From FLAMINGOS ON THE ROOF: POEMS AND PAINTINGS by Calef Brown. Reprinted by permission of Houghton Mifflin Harcourt Publishing Company. All rights reserved. **MY SISTER** copyright © Margaret Mahy. Reproduced by permission of Watson, Little Ltd. **THE COBRA'S CRIMBO** copyright © 1984, 1987 Kit Wright. From CAT AMONG THE PIGEONS by Kit Wright (Viking Kestrel, 1987). **THE RED-HAIRED MAN** by Daniil Kharms & translated by Neil Cornwell. Reproduced by permission of Profile Books Ltd. **BORDERLINE CASE** copyright © Colin West. Reproduced by permission of the author. **PUMPKIN-GRUMPKIN** copyright © Sampurna Chattarji. Reproduced by